is both valuable and important to a child's later development, and this is found, for instance, in *Finger Rhymes*, the first book of the eight book series.

This series provides an enjoyable introduction to poetry, music and dance for every young child. Most books of this type have only a few rhymes for each age group, whereas each book of this series is intended for a particular age group. There is a strong teaching sequence in the selection of rhymes, from the first simple ways of winning the child's interest by toe tapping and palm tickling jingles, through practice in numbers, memory and pronunciation, to combining sound, action and words. For the first time young children can learn rhymes in a sequence that is related to their age.

Singing Rhymes

by DOROTHY TAYLOR
with illustrations by
BRIAN PRICE THOMAS
and photographs by JOHN MOYES

Ladybird Books Loughborough

Contents

Page

The farmer's in his den,
The farmer's in his den,
E —— I —— E —— I,
The farmer's in his den.

The farmer wants a wife,
The farmer wants a wife,
E —— I —— E —— I,
The farmer wants a wife.

The wife wants a child, etc.
The child wants a nurse, etc.
The nurse wants a dog, etc.
We all pat the dog, etc.

Children form a ring.

Verse 1: A child, as farmer, skips around the middle of the ring, while others skip and sing.

2: Farmer chooses a wife and takes her into the middle.

3: Wife chooses a child, etc.

4: Child chooses a nurse, etc.

5: Nurse chooses a dog, etc.

6: Everyone gently *pats the dog, who becomes the farmer when the game starts again.*

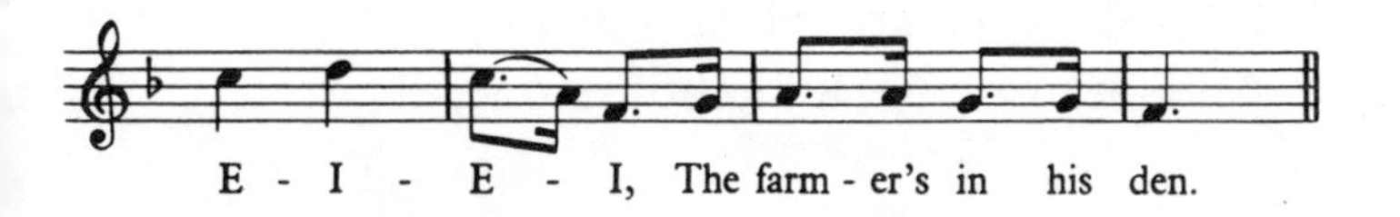

Poor Jenny sits a-weeping,
A-weeping, a-weeping,
Poor Jenny sits a-weeping
On a bright summer's day.

Pray tell us what you're weeping for,
What you're weeping for, what you're weeping for,
Pray tell us . . . etc.

I'm weeping for a sweetheart,
A sweetheart, a sweetheart, etc.

Pray stand ye up and choose one,
And choose one, and choose one, etc.

Verses 1 to 4
Poor Jen - ny sits a - weep-ing, a - weep-ing, a - weep-ing, Poor
Jen - ny sits a - weep - ing On a bright sum - mer's day.

(Change of tune)
Now you're married we wish you joy,
First a girl and then a boy,
Seven years after, son and daughter,
Pray young couple come kiss together.
. . . Kiss her once, kiss her twice, kiss her three times over . . .

Children form a ring:
Verse 1: Girl sits in centre of a ring, hands over face, while ring of children dance round singing.
2: All stand still and sing.
3: Jenny replies.
4: Children in ring dance and sing.
5: Jenny chooses a partner and dances with him, while rest of children stand and clap in time to the music.

There was a jolly miller, and he lived by himself,
As the wheel went round he made his wealth;
One hand in the hopper, the other in the bag,
As the wheel went round he made his grab.

An uneven number of players stand arm in arm, in pairs. The 'odd' man out is the 'miller' who stands in the centre of a double ring which marches round and round while the verse is sung. At the word 'grab', each child on the inside of the ring leaves his partner and moves quickly forward to 'grab' the arm of the child in the outer circle one couple ahead. At the same time, the 'miller' grabs whoever he can. The spare child becomes the next 'miller'.

There was a jol-ly mil-ler and he lived by him self, As the

wheel went round he__made his wealth; One hand in the hop-per, the

o-ther in the bag, As the wheel went round he__ made his grab.

Sally, Sally Waters, sprinkle in the pan,
Rise Sally, rise Sally, and choose your young man.
Bow to the East, bow to the West,
Choose for the worst, choose for the best
And bow to the one that you love best.

A ring is formed and in the middle sits a girl pretending to weep. The ring dances round, singing. At the word 'rise', the child in the centre chooses the one she likes best by curtseying before her choice, and the chosen partner goes into the centre. While the marriage formula is sung the two in the middle dance together while the other children continue to dance round. The game can then be repeated at will, the chosen partner taking the place of the original child in the middle.

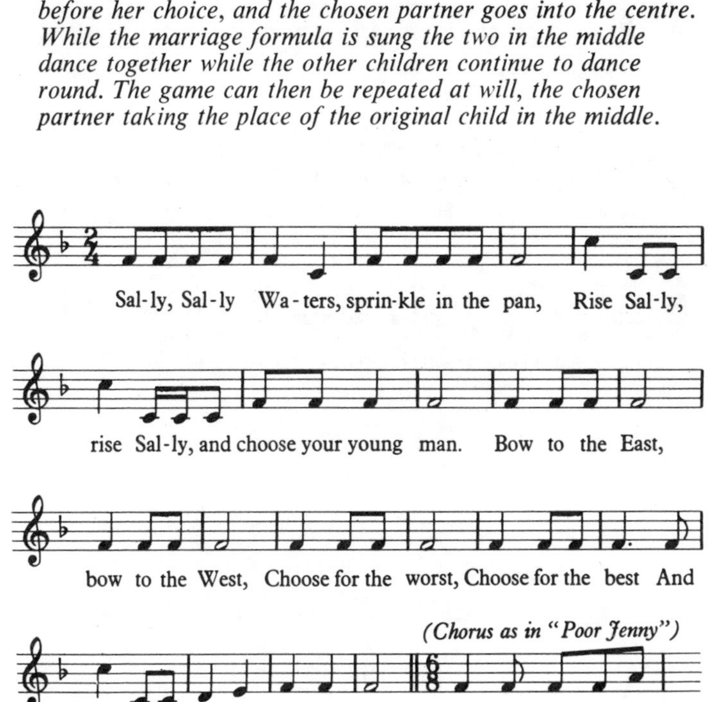

Marriage Formula

Now you're married we wish you joy,
First a girl and then a boy,
Seven years after, son and daughter;
Pray young couple come kiss together.

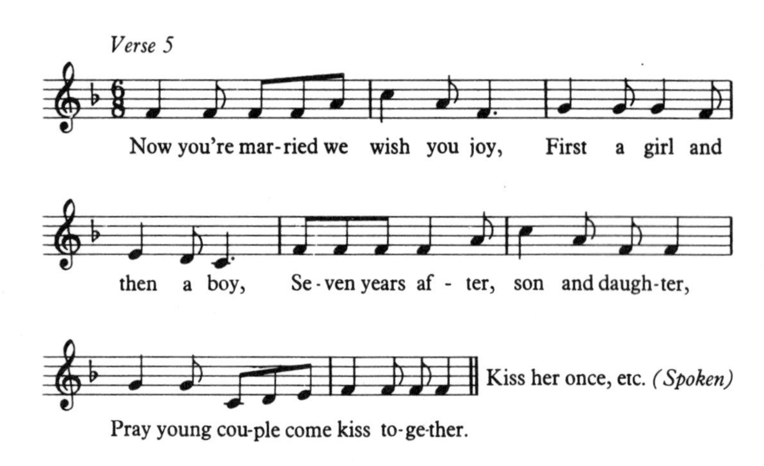

Wallflowers, wallflowers,
Growing up so high,
All you young ladies
Are meant to die.
Excepting little . . . . .
She is the best of all.
She can skip, and she can dance,
And she can turn the candlestick.
O my, fie for shame,
Turn your back to the wall again.

The children form a ring by joining hands, then dance slowly round, singing the words. When a girl is named by the ring she turns round so that her face is turned to the outside of the ring and her back to the inside. She still clasps hands with those on either side and dances round with them. This action is repeated until all the players have been named and turned face outwards.

Old Roger is dead and lies in his grave,
Lies in his grave, lies in his grave.
Old Roger is dead and lies in his grave,
Heigh ho, lies in his grave.

They planted an apple tree over his head,
Over his head, over his head.
They planted an apple tree over his head,
Heigh ho, over his head.

The apples grew ripe and they all fell off,
All fell off, all fell off.
The apples grew ripe and they all fell off,
Heigh ho, all fell off.

There came an old woman a-picking them up,
Picking them up, picking them up, etc.

Old Roger got up and gave her a knock,
Gave her a knock, gave her a knock, etc.

Which made the old woman go hippety-hop,
Go hippety-hop, go hippety-hop, etc.

Verse 1: The children form a ring, one child lies in the centre.
2: Mime the planting of a tree.
3: Mime the shedding of apples from the tree.
4: One child pretends to pick up apples and put them in an apron.
5: Roger gets up and nudges her, while chasing her round the ring.
6: Old woman hops all round the ring.

3 *Mime the shedding of apples from the tree.*

4 *One child pretends to pick up apples and put them in an apron.*

5 *Roger gets up and nudges her, while chasing her round the ring.*

6 *Old woman hops all round the ring.*

Briar Rosebud was a pretty child,
A pretty child, a pretty child.
Briar Rosebud was a pretty child, a pretty child.

We pray you Rosebud please take care,
Please take care, please take care.
We pray you Rosebud please take care,
Please take care.

The children form a ring.
Verse 1: Chosen girl skips inside ring alone.
2: Children point outside of ring to where an old woman (wicked fairy in disguise) is lurking.

Briar Rose bud was a pret - ty child, a
pret-ty child, a pret - ty child, Briar Rose-bud was a
pret - ty child, a pret - ty child.

There creeps a wicked fairy now, etc.
Her spell says Rosebud she shall die, etc.
A shining fairy now appears, etc.
She breaks the wicked fairy's spell, etc.
Briar Rosebud sleep a hundred years, etc.
A hedge grows up so tall and thick, etc.
A Prince comes by, a king's own son, etc.
Briar Rosebud, please wake up again, etc.
Briar Rosebud wakens joyfully, etc.
We all dance at the wedding feast, etc.

3: Old woman enters ring and creeps round.
4: Old woman points at Briar Rosebud, who sinks to ground.
5: Another child gaily skips into ring.
6: She waves a pretend wand over Briar Rosebud who is lying peacefully on ground.
7: Fairy stands still with uplifted wand over the sleeping Briar Rosebud.
8: Children close ring to make a thick bush round Briar Rosebud.
9: Boy gallops on horse around the outside.
10: Ring opens, and the children make arches while walking backwards slowly. Prince enters and kisses Briar Rosebud, who wakes up.
11: Prince and Briar Rosebud dance together.
12: Children dance in pairs.

3

6

8

10

Oats and beans and barley grow,
Oats and beans and barley grow,
But not you nor I nor anyone knows
How oats and beans and barley grow.

First the farmer sows his seed,
Then he stands and takes his ease,
Stamps his feet and claps his hands,
And turns around to view the land.

Oats and beans and barley grow, etc.

Players form ring – farmer in middle.
Chorus: All dance round, farmer skipping in the middle.
Verse 1: Everyone mimes words with the farmer.
Chorus: All dance round, farmer skipping in the middle.

Oats and beans and bar - ley grow, Oats and beans and
bar - ley grow, But not you nor I nor a - ny one knows how
oats and beans and bar - ley grow.

Waiting for a partner,
Waiting for a partner,
Open the ring and take one in,
And kiss her in the centre.

Oats and beans and barley grow, etc.

Now you're married you must obey,
You must be true in all you say,
You must be kind, you must be good,
And help your wife to chop the wood.

Oats and beans and barley grow, etc.

2: Farmer chooses partner.

Chorus: Farmer and wife dance together, while others dance round.

3: Players wag forefingers at wife and farmer as they sing.

Chorus: Farmer and wife dance together, while others dance round.

The big ship sails down the Illy Ally O,
The Illy Ally O, the Illy Ally O,
The big ship sails down the Illy Ally O,
On the last day of September.

The big ship sails too slow, too slow,
Too slow, too slow, too slow, too slow,
The big ship sails too slow, too slow,
On the last day of September.

The Captain said, 'It will never, never do,
Never never do, never never do,' etc.

The big ship sank to the bottom of the sea,
The bottom of the sea, the bottom of the sea, etc.

We all dip our heads in the deep blue sea,
The deep blue sea, the deep blue sea, etc.

All children hold hands in a long line. One child at the end puts his arm up against a wall to make an arch. The child at the other end leads the rest of the line under the arch so that the child making the arch is twisted round until his arms are crossed. Then the 'leader' of the line goes through his arch and that of his neighbour so that the neighbour twists round as the last child goes through. This is repeated while the first verse only is sung again and again until all children have crossed arms.

Verse 2: First and last child form ring by joining their crossed hands. Verse is sung at slow speed.

3: Shake heads gravely.

4: Slowly squat and rise again.

5: Bend heads down as low as possible.

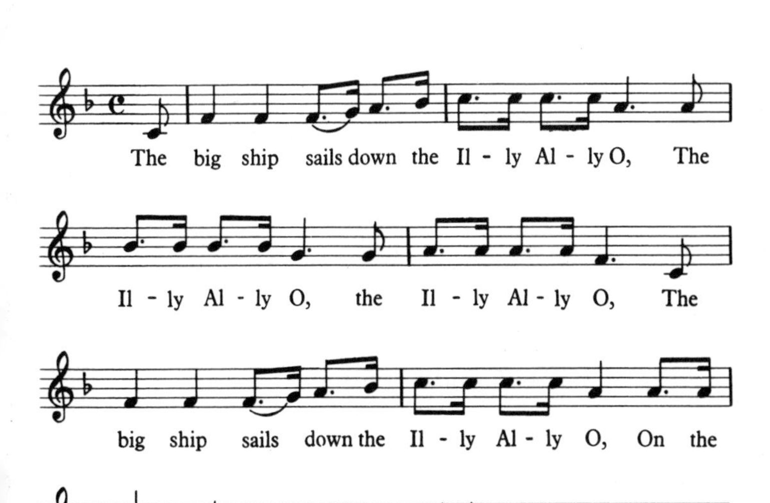
The big ship sails down the Il - ly Al - ly O, The
Il - ly Al - ly O, the Il - ly Al - ly O, The
big ship sails down the Il - ly Al - ly O, On the
last day of Sep - tem - ber.

Have you any bread and wine?
We are the rovers:
Have you any bread and wine?
For we're the gallant soldiers.

Yes, we have some bread and wine,
We are the rovers:
Yes, we have some bread and wine
For we're the gallant soldiers.

Shall we have one glass of it?
We are the rovers:
Shall we have one glass of it?
For we're the gallant soldiers.

The second and fourth lines are the same throughout the song. The first line is repeated for the third line.

One glass of it you shall not have, etc.

We shall send for the redcoat men, etc.

What care we for the redcoat men? etc.

We shall send for the bluecoat men, etc.

What care we for the bluecoat men? etc.

Buckle up your sleeves and we'll have a fight, etc.

Players line up in two rows. Each row advances a few paces, sings its verse and then retreats, each singing alternate verses. At the last verse, both rows advance, and a mock battle takes place.

Have you a - ny bread and wine? We are the rov - ers:

Have you a - ny bread and wine? For we're the gal - lant sol - diers.

Here we come gathering nuts in May,
Nuts in May, nuts in May,
Here we come gathering nuts in May,
On a cold and frosty morning.

Who will you have for nuts in May, etc.

We'll have . . . . . for nuts in May, etc.

Who will you send to fetch her away, etc.

We'll have . . . . . to fetch her away, etc.

Verse 1: Two lines are formed, and stand facing each other. Both lines skip forwards, then back.
2: Line one advances, asking the question.
3: The other line chooses a child and advances.
4: First line dances forward and asks question.
5: Line two answers.
Then the chosen two have a tug of war until one child is pulled to the other side and is then a member of that team.

Here we come gath er - ing nuts in May, nuts in May,
nuts in May, Here we come gath er - ing nuts in May, on a
cold and fros - ty morn - ing.

Row: 1 How many miles to Babylon?
2 Three score and ten.
1 Shall I be there by candlelight?
2 Yes, and back again.
1 Open the gates and let us through.
2 Not without a curtsey and bow.
1 There's the curtsey, there's the bow,
Open the gates and let us through.

Players form into two rows facing each other, row 1 singing first line, row 2 the second and so on. For the curtsey, row 1 bend back, and for the bow they lean forward. At the demand 'open the gates and let us through', row 2 lift arms high to form arches, and those in row 1 rush through their uplifted arms. Row 1 now becomes Row 2, row 2 becomes row 1, and the game re-starts.

How ma-ny miles to Ba - by - lon? Three score and ten. Shall

I be there by can - dle - light? Yes and back a - gain.

O-pen the gates and let us through, Not with-out a curt-sey and bow.

There's the curt- sey, there's the bow, Open the gates and let us through.

Here come three dukes a-riding,
A-riding, a-riding,
Here come three dukes a-riding,
With a rancy, tancy, tay!

What is your good will, sirs?
Will, sirs, will, sirs?
What is your good will, sirs?
With a rancy, tancy, tay!

Our good will is to marry,
To marry, to marry,
Our good will is to marry,
With a rancy, tancy, tay!

Marry one of us, sirs,
Us, sirs, us, sirs,
Marry one of us, sirs,
With a rancy, tancy, tay!

You're all too fat and dirty,
Dirty, dirty,
You're all too fat and dirty,
With a rancy, tancy, tay!

We're good enough for you, sirs,
You, sirs, you, sirs,
We're good enough for you, sirs,
With a rancy, tancy, tay!

You're all as stiff as pokers,
Pokers, pokers,
You're all as stiff as pokers,
With a rancy, tancy, tay!

We can bend as much as you, sirs,
You, sirs, you, sirs,
We can bend as much as you, sirs,
With a rancy, tancy, tay!

Through the kitchen and down the hall,
I choose the fairest of you all,
The fairest one that I can see
Is pretty Miss. . . . . , walk with me.

Three children are chosen to be three dukes. The rest of the players represent maidens, forming a line facing the line of dukes. Each line in turn advances and retires singing its part, beginning with the "three dukes" singing the first verse.

Verse 4: Maidens curtsey and look coyly at the dukes.

6: Maidens draw themselves up stiffly and sing indignantly.

8: They bend and bow very low.

Last verse: A "duke" brings one of the maidens to join their line.

The game then continues by all four singing, 'Here come four *dukes', 'Here come* five *dukes', etc., until all are ranged on one side.*

Here come three dukes a - rid - ing, A - rid - ing, a -

- rid - ing Here come three dukes a - rid - ing, with a

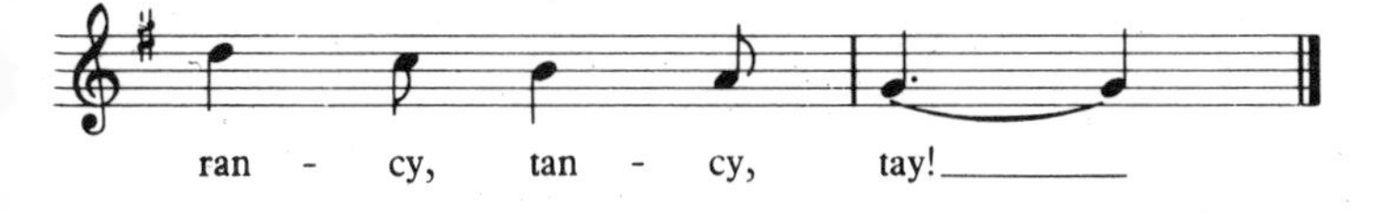
ran - cy, tan - cy, tay!

See the robbers passing by,
Passing by, passing by:
See the robbers passing by
My fair lady.

What have the robbers done to you,
Done to you, done to you,
What have the robbers done to you
My fair lady?

Two children clasp hands and form an arch, having decided beforehand who is to be 'golden' and who 'silver'. (This refers to the lost shoe.)

Verse 1: Players each dance under and through the arch singing. At the end the 'arch' captures a child and, rocking her to and fro, sings verse 2.

2: Sung by couple making arch.

3: Sung by the prisoner.

4: Sung by everyone. At the end the prisoner is taken aside and quietly asked to choose 'golden' or 'silver'. She stands behind her choice. When all have been captured in this way there is then a tug-of-war.

Stole my comb and lost my shoe
Lost my shoe, lost my shoe:
Stole my comb and lost my shoe
My fair lady.

Off to prison you must go,
You must go, you must go:
Off to prison you must go
My fair lady.

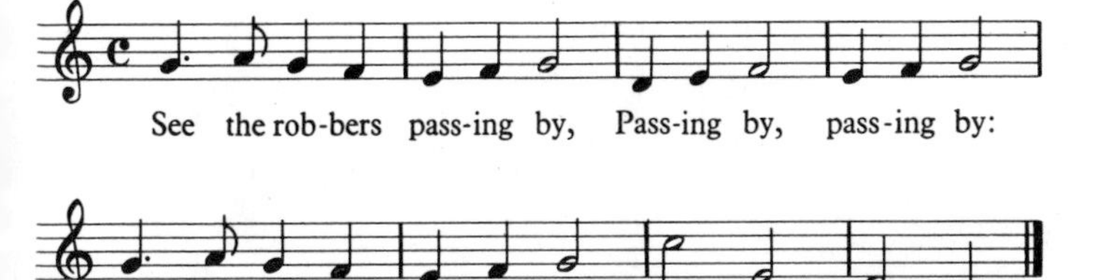

Oranges and lemons,
Say the bells of St Clement's;
You owe me five farthings,
Say the bells of St Martin's;
When will you pay me?
Say the bells of Old Bailey;
When I grow rich,
Say the bells of Shoreditch;
When will that be?
Say the bells of Stepney;
I'm sure I don't know,
Says the Great Bell of Bow.

Or-ang-es and lem-ons, say the bells of St. Cle-ment's, You
owe me five far-things say the bells of St. Mar - tin's;
When will you pay me? Say the bells of Old Bai - ley;
When I grow rich, Say the bells of Shore - ditch; When will that
be? Say the bells of Step - ney; I'm sure I don't know, says the
(Spoken)
Great Bell of Bow. Here comes a candle to light you to bed etc.

Here comes a candle to light you to bed;
Here comes a chopper to chop off your head;
The last, last, last, last man's head.

Two of the older children make an arch, one to be 'Orange,' the other 'Lemon'. The other children form a line and skip under the arch. The speed quickens on 'here comes a candle', and on the last line the arch 'chop' with their arms until they reach the words 'last man's head', when they encircle a child who must choose to join the side of 'Orange' or 'Lemon'. (This must be whispered to prevent the rest of the children from knowing which is which.) The game is repeated until all have chosen sides, when there is a general tug of war.

London Bridge is falling down,
Falling down, falling down,
London Bridge is falling down,
My fair lady.

Build it up with iron bars,
Iron bars, iron bars,
Build it up with iron bars,
My fair lady.

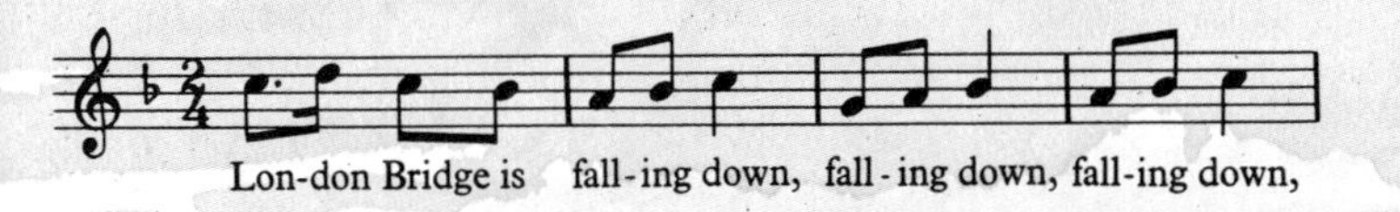
Lon-don Bridge is fall-ing down, fall-ing down, fall-ing down,

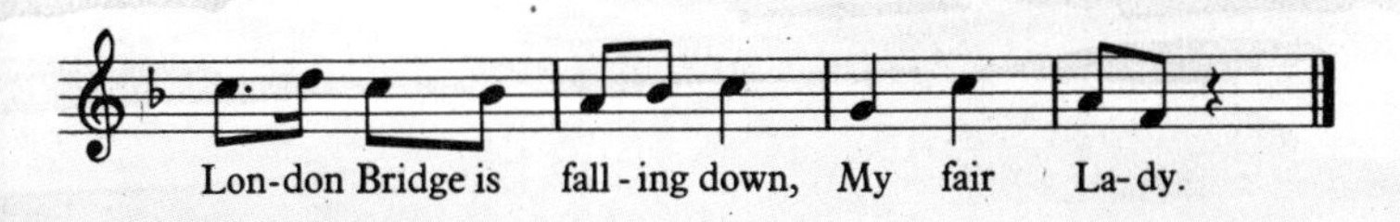
Lon-don Bridge is fall-ing down, My fair La-dy.

London Bridge is falling down *(continued)*

Iron bars will bend and bow, etc.

Build it up with pins and needles, etc.

Pins and needles will rust and bend, etc.

Build it up with penny loaves, etc.

Penny loaves will tumble down, etc.

Here's a prisoner I have got, etc.

What's the prisoner done to you, etc.

Stole my watch and broke my chain, etc.

What'll you take to set him free, etc.

Ten hundred pounds will set him free, etc.

Ten hundred pounds we have not got, etc.

Then off to prison he must go, etc.

Two children join hands to form an arch and the other children skip through singing each verse until verse 8. In this verse the pair making the arch catch one of the children and hold him while the others stand round in a circle. This position is maintained until verse 14, when the prisoner is taken out of the circle and the game can resume, with a new couple making the arch.

BOOK ONE

Finger Rhymes

A selection of finger counting and other rhymes to exercise the young child's mind and body.

BOOK TWO

Number Rhymes

This book brings together many familiar and some less well known rhymes which help with the first steps of arithmetic.

BOOK THREE

Memory Rhymes

A diverse collection of rhymes mainly concerned with days of the week, months of the year, points of the compass and letters of the alphabet.

BOOK FOUR

Talking Rhymes

Humorous and other verses providing practice in pronunciation, including many of the better known tongue-twisters.